THE CHINESE INK STICK

The New Year Callers

THE
CHINESE INK STICK

TEXT AND DRAWINGS BY

KURT WIESE

DOUBLEDAY, DORAN AND COMPANY, INC.

GARDEN CITY　　　MCMXLII　　　NEW YORK

CONTENTS

CHAPTER   PAGE

I. THE WELL OF HEAVENLY WISDOM .   3

II. THE TIGER AND THE TURTLE . . .   9

III. THE BAMBOO PAINTER   17

IV. WU TAO TZU   27

V. WITH THE LETTER WRITER . . .   39

v

CONTENTS

CHAPTER

PAGE

VI. Mr. Lee 47

VII. On Our Street 55

VIII. The Harbor and River Life . . 63

IX. A Brave River Man 75

X. Cheaters Cheated 87

XI. I Am Lost and Found Again . . 103

XII. At the Tea Merchant's 117

XIII. Meng from Ningpo 129

XIV. I Am Discovered 137

XV. The Spring Festival 143

XVI. At Home with Liang 149

XVII. A Long Journey 161

XVIII. The New Year 177

XIX. School Days 183

XX. Rumors of War 197

ILLUSTRATIONS

IN COLOR

The New Year Callers . . . . . . *Frontispiece*

PAGE

His brush ran over the paper with fast strokes . 21

The two assistants took the letter 93

He walked hundreds of miles with his old mother on his back 131

IN BLACK AND WHITE

"Well," said the tiger, "now I have you." . . . 11

He began at once, and in a short time had finished the painting of a braying donkey 31

The letter writer had a customer 41

The cormorant fisher 59

The temple of the ten thousand gods 67

In a moment the whole port was a mass of flames 79

Up went the table and down went everything . 111

The "Moon View" 123

The beak and eye of the bird are being done with his pointed finger nails 155

On the lake 169

Chinese characters 190

THE WELL OF HEAVENLY WISDOM

CHAPTER I

THE WELL OF HEAVENLY WISDOM

RAIN is pouring down and I am lying in the middle of the wet road. Squish—squash—squish—go the feet of the coolies carrying their burdens. Then with a whining noise comes a massive wooden wheel and digs itself deep into the soft ground. I am there right on the spot, and the wheel presses me deeper and deeper into the ground. For I am only a little piece of black Chinese ink, half an inch long.

Now I cannot see the sky any more, nor the people nor the green ricefields. I rest under a cover of mud and am all alone with my thoughts.

I was not always as small as I am to-day. By no means! Once I was—oh, five inches long, the edges of me sharp cut. I was made out of the famous black earth called *"Hei Du"* after a several thousand year old receipt. I was very black. But on the front of me were golden letters saying, "The Well of Heavenly Wisdom," and on my back there was a golden dragon. Now this is all gone; I am only a little stump, and what has gone has been transformed by skillful hands into writing and pictures.

Ah, those were wonderful times when I was young and shiny. After leaving the factory I went to Mr. Lo Ho Chiang, a dealer in writing materials. He put me on a red lacquered tray so

4

THE W...
that every...body could see me. Next to the tray
there s...ood a bamboo cup holding a bunch of
h...s. Proud writing brushes. They were so

proud that they held their heads stiff and upright,
just as if they were pointed arrows going into
war. But I knew better. I knew that when you
dipped them into water their proud heads would
become soft and would bow whenever they
touched the paper. I often teased them and said:

5

"Now, now, don't be so proud; wait till you are dipped into water and the hands of men make you work!" But they were at no loss for an answer, and they would say, "Wait till you get into water and hands rub you. Then you will lose your feet, and more and more, until there is nothing left of you. When we are still here you will be gone—gone altogether."

I did not like this talk and kept hoping that nobody would buy me.

THE TIGER AND THE TURTLE

CHAPTER II

THE TIGER AND THE TURTLE

BUT I must tell you more about that bamboo cup. It had a picture carved all around it, and a little story, too. The picture showed a fierce tiger putting his paw on the back of a turtle, while the turtle had her head and legs hidden under her shell. And this is the story:

9

The tiger is a very impatient animal, but the turtle has all the patience in the world. And this is easy to understand, because the tiger is everybody's enemy, and men go out to kill him. Even if he is not killed he does not live longer than thirty years, so he has to hurry and make as much as possible out of his short life. Turtles, on the other hand, live for several hundred years, and nobody can harm them because they are well protected by their shells.

Now this tiger, who was a very fierce one, used to drink from the same pool every day. A nice clear pool it was; but whenever he leaned down to take a drink the turtle used to stir up the mud. Then the tiger would get his mouth full of mud, which he did not like. So he became very angry at the turtle and swore that he would kill her if ever he met her on his way.

And one day he actually did meet her. It was spring, and the turtle had a strong desire for a

"Well," said the tiger, "now I have you"

few bites of fresh leaves. She swam ashore and began to nibble peacefully the tender leaves which had just opened on the bank of the pool. At that very moment the tiger came down for a sip of water. He had hunted along the salt lake all day, and his mouth and whiskers were all salty. And if he didn't see the turtle on the pool's bank! One jump and he landed with his paws on her back, but the turtle pulled her head, feet, and tail into her shell and was safe.

"Well," said the tiger, "now I have you. I know your shell is hard and I cannot break it with my teeth, but I will wait. I will hold you with my paws until you come out if it takes hours or days or even weeks."

The turtle was not disturbed at all. She calmly closed her eyes, and as she closed them she said, "What of it? I may just as well take a two years' nap. So long, Mr. Tiger."

The tiger waited for three days, but the turtle

remained quietly sleeping. At last, weak with hunger, when he thought no one was looking, the tiger quietly lifted his paws and stole away. That was the story written in pictures on the bamboo cup.

THE BAMBOO PAINTER

CHAPTER III

THE BAMBOO PAINTER

ONE day a shadow fell on the red lacquer tray, and two big glasses in a pair of spectacles bent over and peered at me. Then pointed fingers with long nails covered with horn cases took me up and held me to the light. I heard prices named—200 cash, then 150, then 175. Suddenly I was rolled up in red paper, and I

17

disappeared into a dark bag. A little while afterward I rolled out of the wrapper and looked around, wondering where I was.

Now I knew. I was on the table of the famous painter of bamboo, Kao Ko Kung. How often had I heard of him. The brushes in the dealer's shop often spoke of him and were most eager to be bought by him. He was very old, more than seventy. All his life he had painted bamboo. For in my country an artist paints the same subject again and again, until he has made it as perfect as he knows how.

Many painters never reach their goal, and they die unsatisfied. But Kao Ko Kung did not belong with them. His pictures were in great demand, and many a rich merchant would sit down at night with a picture by Kao Ko Kung before him. In China a picture is rolled up and kept on a shelf. When its owner wishes to look at the picture he does not open the scroll at once to its full

extent, but little by little, so that only twelve to
eighteen inches of it can be seen at a time. He
wishes to enjoy bit by bit the wonderful details

which would be overlooked if the whole were
seen at once.

Now I could see the famous master at his work.
First he took me up with his pointed fingers,
looked me over carefully, and then—he dipped

my feet into cold water. How strange—I lost all feeling in them. Next he put them down on a black slate tray and rubbed and rubbed. "Mercy's sake," I thought, "there go my feet." The water around them turned black, and one little speck after another was rubbed off my feet. Before I was fully aware of what had happened the artist put me down again. A brush was dipped into the black liquid. Then I saw the master bend down, his lips quivering with emotion, while his brush ran over the paper with fast strokes.

The paper had a fine yellow tint, and presently the bamboo leaves stood out beautifully black against the mellow background, as against an evening sky, and a light wind seemed to stir them.

Toward evening the master put his brush down. The hour had come when he awaited his friends. For he lived on the hill, and every night when the light breeze blew up from the river, his

His brush ran over the paper with fast strokes

friends would gather to enjoy the cool air and to drink their tea with the venerable one.

This night they brought up an old picture, painted by China's greatest painter, who lived in the Seventh Century and whose name was Wu Tao Tzu. And if you read farther you will find what I heard about the life of this artist.

WU TAO TZU

CHAPTER IV

WU TAO TZU

WHEN Wu was very young the Emperor called him to court, for he worked faster than anybody else and was equally talented in every subject. One day the Emperor had a longing to see the scenery of the Chia Ling River in the province of Szechuan, and so he ordered Wu

27

to go to that place and paint it. It was a long journey over roads, channels, rivers, and lakes, and it was several months before Wu came back. When he arrived at the palace the Emperor was very eager to see his sketches and asked for them. But Wu answered: "I have no sketches; it is all in my heart." Then he went into one of the halls of the palace and in a single day tossed off a hundred miles of landscape.

On his voyage to the Chia Ling River Wu had had to pass through a district which was in revolt against the government. The dam of the river had burst, and the relief money which the government had promised had not arrived. Thus the Emperor's passport did not help Wu much. No one wanted him as a guest, and he was compelled to knock at the door of a monastery and ask the monks for a night's lodging. But even the monks were inhospitable. They told him they had no room to spare and that he would have to spend the night in the courtyard among the animals and the servants of a caravan from the north. He said he would gladly accept this shelter and promised to decorate one of the walls of the monastery with a picture. Wu did not sleep much that night; the camels were grunting, and the donkeys were braying. When at last morning dawned he got up and tried to get a breakfast. But they served him only salted beans without curd. After his meal he was led to a white temple wall to start on his picture. He began at once, and in a short time had finished the painting of a braying donkey. After that he left.

The following morning the monks found that all the furniture and art objects in the room where the donkey was painted on the wall had been kicked to pieces. The priests were sure this was Wu's handiwork, so they ran after him. Far outside the city on the road they caught up with him and told him of the happenings of the night before. They begged him to return and to erase the drawing. He agreed to this if they would take him back in a sedan chair and offer him all the hospitality due a great artist. They were willing to do this, and after he had erased the painting there was no more trouble in the temple, and Wu continued his voyage.

When Wu reached old age the Emperor ordered him to paint a landscape of considerable dimensions on the wall of the Ming Huang Palace. The artist prepared his materials and, concealing the wall behind a curtain, began his work. After a little while he drew aside the curtain. There before the eyes of the Emperor lay the most glorious scene those eyes had ever gazed upon—mountains and forests, clouds and men, flowers and birds, all of the greatest perfection. While the Emperor was looking upon it with admiration Wu pointed to a certain spot in the picture, showing a temple

He began at once, and in a short time had finished the painting of a braying donkey

grotto at the foot of a mountain. "Behold this grotto, O Emperor! Within it dwells the spirit leading to eternal happiness." With these words he clapped his hands, and the gate of the temple suddenly opened. "The interior is beautiful beyond conception," continued the artist. "Permit me to lead the way so that Your Majesty's eyes may see the marvels it contains." With these words he entered the gate of the grotto and turned around, beckoning his patron to follow. But at that instant the gateway closed, and before the amazed monarch could advance a step the whole scene faded away, leaving the wall as white as if the painter's brush had never touched it.

And Wu Tzu was never seen again.

Days passed in the studio of the bamboo painter. I noticed with horror that my feet were all rubbed off. The brushes in Lo Ho Chiang's shop had been right. I could see myself disappearing. One morning, as the master held me between his fingers and began rubbing me on the slate tray, I became so frightened that I used all my strength to oppose further rubbing. I was so energetic that I made a noise on the tray. When the master heard the noise he stopped, looked at me, and frowned. Then he threw me aside and called his servant.

"Take this piece of ink away," he said. "I don't

want to use it any more: there is grit mixed with the ink."

The servant picked me up and dropped me into his pocket. When he had finished his work he made his way to a certain street and before long stopped at the desk of a public letter writer and offered me for sale. Only a few pieces of cash were paid for me, but I was glad; for now I was put on a tray together with several other pieces, and from my position I could look out and see all the busy life of the street passing right before my eyes.

WITH THE LETTER WRITER

The letter writer had a customer

Our nearest neighbor was a man who dealt in drugs. One could find strange things on his desk: for instance, tiger bones, which, rubbed into powder and mixed with tea, gave strength to the weak. There were deer horns, also in powder form, bought by homely people in the belief that the mixture would make them attractive. There were all sorts of herbs, some taken to make the inside of the body warm, some to make it cool. That is the way a Chinese physician judges a sickness: one's insides are either too hot or too cold.

Above all the druggist loved music, and he often played on a violin that had only one string. He kept a nightingale in a cage, and in the morning, when the sun peeped over the roofs right into our corner, the druggist covered the cage with a piece of cloth, leaving just a little opening for the sun to creep into the cage. I could then see the shining eyes of the bird. Perhaps he thought that he was sitting among the shady leaves of a tree, for he would begin to sing very sweetly, while the druggist played on the violin. It was the loveliest duet in the world.

Our neighbor on the other side of the street was a big rice merchant.

His name was Lee, which means "plum." But don't think for a moment that this name is funny to the Chinese. As a matter of fact, the name of Lee is one of the best in the country. The Chinese have only two hundred family names, you know. So you will find many Lees and Los or Wus. And the family name always comes first. There are many stories about these families. I will tell you one about a Mr. Lee.

MR. LEE

CHAPTER VI

MR. LEE

MR. LEE was a very successful business man, but he had started all wrong. This is the story of how he came to be a business man.

When Lee was a little boy he did not like hard work. But his father was very poor and could not give him an education. Instead, when Lee was twelve years old his father apprenticed him to a rope maker to learn the art of making ropes. This was a very hard trade, for the twines from which the ropes were twisted were as sharp as wires, and very soon the little boy suffered from bleeding hands. The master was a very hard man. He did not pay any attention to the little boy's suffering, but punished him because he made no progress.

One day, when the boy had again made only a small piece of rope, not longer than a foot in a whole day's work, the master became very angry and said: "I give you one more day. If by that time you have not finished a piece of rope which is longer than my measure I shall send you back to your father, and he will have to pay me for all the material and the time you have wasted."

The next day the little boy sat in the corner struggling hard with the rope, but it did not become longer. When it was time to deliver it to the master his heart sank and tears rolled down his cheeks. But through tears and despair he suddenly was struck with an idea. He took a small piece of rope and tied the two ends together.

Then he took it to his master and said cheerfully:
"Look, Master, at the lot of rope I have
twisted. I measure it continually and I am not
able to reach the end."

The master looked at the ring in the boy's hand
and became so angry that his face was all red.

"You silly boy," he said, "you have tied the two
ends together and there are now no ends. But,"
he continued, "this is enough for me. Take the
rope and leave my house at once. You are worth-
less!"

The boy took the rope and ran away, but not
to his father's hut.

On his way he met a traveling potter. The rope
with which the potter had fastened his wares on
his back was broken, and he offered the boy a pot
in exchange for the rope. The boy took the pot
and went on his way.

Soon he met a woman at a spring. She had just
filled a pot with water and put it on her head. As

she turned around the pot fell from her head and broke. She offered the boy a bag of barley for his pot. The boy exchanged the pot for the barley and traveled on. That night he stopped at an inn, and awoke the next morning to find that the bag of barley had disappeared. He demanded the restoration of his property, but the innkeeper, who had no barley, offered him a bag of rice.

He took the bag of rice and traveled on and on, living on a few handfuls of rice from the bag.

One day he came to a district where there had been a severe drought. The first crop of the year was destroyed, and the people had no seed for the second one, so they asked him to give them his bag of rice. The boy said he would if they would give him one tenth of the crop.

To this the people agreed.

Soon after the sowing rain began to fall, and the weather was just right for rice. After two months all the fields were full of ripe rice plants —there had never been a harvest like that year's.

The boy's share was worth a thousand dollars. So he took his share and traveled back to his home town to open a rice store. Since he was intelligent and full of new ideas he became successful, and his business increased year by year. Our Mr. Lee became one of the most important men of the town.

ON OUR STREET

CHAPTER VII

ON OUR STREET

THE street traffic passed right in front of my desk. Early in the morning when we opened our business by putting up the roof, the water carriers came up the steps, each with two buckets of water. Soon after them came the carriers of rice, unloading rice from the ships into Lee's store. They carried the rice in two baskets, fastened one at each end of a bamboo pole, which rested on their shoulders. These baskets were very clean, and the rice in them was heaped to the top. Over the rice was a layer of flour on which was stamped a pattern, so that the receiver could see at once whether anything had been stolen from the basket. For if the coolie were to take only a few grains the pattern would break and the basket would be refused.

Our streets are so narrow that a carriage cannot pass through them. All burdens are carried by men, and he who wants to ride has to take a ricksha or a sedan chair. Everybody has to get out of the way of the sedan chair, because it is the heavier. Two coolies carry the chair on their shoulders; a third one goes along for relief. When the coolies are trotting along at their fast pace, they are unable to stop if anything crosses their path. Therefore they have the right of way.

Every morning an old woman passed our desk, carrying a small basket with strange tools. They were little hooks set in wooden handles. The woman shouted in a high-pitched voice: "*Ya tschung! Ya tschung!*" This means tooth worm. When anyone in the street had a toothache he would call for the woman, and she would pull the nerve out of the hollow tooth. The people think that the nerve is a worm which enters a tooth by boring a hole into it.

Early in the morning there appeared also the fishermen. They often came to our desk and proudly showed us the contents of their buckets. Mr. Wu sometimes bought a fish, hung it in the shade, and took it home at night. On these occasions I would hear how the fish were caught.

Fastened to the sides of the fishermen's boats are long poles; on these poles sit big black birds called cormorants. Around its neck each bird has a brass ring, so that it cannot swallow the fish it catches. When the bird comes out of the water with the fish in its beak it at once returns to the boat. The fisherman takes the fish and in return rewards the bird with a small fish which he can swallow in spite of the ring around his neck. After that the bird goes back to the bamboo pole and looks attentively into the water until he detects a new catch.

Toward the late afternoon the birds become tired and don't want to leave the poles; but the fishermen push them off their perches and, if they still remain lazy, give them a spanking, whereupon the birds begin to dive anew for fish.

As soon as the sun sinks, all the boats return to the port. It is a strange sight to see the many boats crowded with the dark figures of the sleeping birds.

The cormorant fisher

THE HARBOR AND RIVER LIFE

CHAPTER VIII

THE HARBOR AND RIVER LIFE

NO WONDER that I liked the place near the harbor. Not only was there the interesting life of the incoming and outgoing ships; there was also a wide view over the old hills of Wuchang on the other side of the Han River. Right at the corner where the Han ended in the

Yangtze Kiang a big trade in lumber went on. The enormous rafts built out of lumber were landed there after long months of floating down the river out of the heart of the ancient province of Szetchuan. The people who owned the lumber lived during this time on top of these rafts in little huts made from split bamboo. When the lumber was sold the huts were sold, too, and they for the most part formed the groups of little houses that clustered along the river bank and were sprinkled over the Wuchang hill—that hill crowned by the temple of the ten thousand gods.

When the Chinese say ten thousand, you must not think that this means the actual number. It is just the way they like to express "a good many." For instance, the name of the Chinese emperors was always Wan Suei, which means the master of ten thousand years. Of course, no emperor lived that long, but each one was supposed to be very wise, as only an old man is.

But whatever the name of the temple, it was very beautiful. It had three roofs, one above the other, the four corners of each swinging upward and ending in the heads of horned dragons.

The roof was covered with shining tiles of yellow and green. They glittered in the sun like a mass of jewels. When you entered the stone gate to the temple you came first to the courtyard, in the middle of which was a square pond. In this pond lived turtles and carps, both of which are considered by the Chinese as growing very old and therefore very wise.

Entering the temple itself, you could go either to the right or the left. Each way was flanked by a stone wall about four feet high. On these walls were ranged one goddess after another—all gilded and with various expressions. Some looked very calm, and there were others whose faces expressed anger and terror. In front of each of the goddesses stood a bronze bowl filled with sand, into which the worshipers put incense sticks. There were hundreds of these sticks sending their fine smoke curls upward. The fine blue haze, hovering around the golden statues, transformed their faces into lifelike images and filled the visitors with that feeling of worship which they needed in front of these immovable, soulless figures.

Along the river bank the most conspicuous things are a number of wooden towers much higher than all the houses around. From the top of each hangs a rope as thick as an arm. These ropes are ship ropes and are twisted from split bamboo. All the Chinese ships use them, and you can see them as a big heap on the forecastles of the Chinese sailboats or junks.

The Chinese shipowners are much too poor to buy hemp rope, so ropes are made from the cheapest material, split bamboo. But bamboo ropes cannot be rolled up like hemp ropes; at the

The temple of the ten thousand gods

start they are very stiff, and the man who makes
them has to go up on one of these towers to find

space for that big inflexible rope which he is
twisting.

Yes, the Chinese boat people are very poor.
You should see the sails of their boats sometimes.

They are patched in many places, and still there are numerous holes left and no money to repair them. Sometimes the sails are mere rags, yet the boats glide along; when you see them against the evening sky they look like bats moving quietly without a flap of the wing.

The boats on the Yangtze Kiang can sail up the river for about eight hundred miles. After that the river becomes very narrow, rushing through sky-high gorges and whirling and foaming around the rocks. The whole population along this part of the river lives by towing boats. Hundreds of the people slip around their shoulders a noose fastened to a long bamboo rope connected with the boat.

Singing a monotonous song they pull the boats while they cling with their bare feet to a small path hewn into the steep rocks that form the river bank. The noose around their shoulders can easily be opened by pulling a little string which runs through a sort of buckle. For if a boat hits a rock and is caught by the whirling current the men are in danger of being pulled down from the high river walls and perishing in the ever hungry waters.

In spite of this precaution many a boat is lost on the way up through the Ichang gorges—also many a man. Still, these people are happy. Their songs, although monotonous, to match their slow, crawling steps, are cheerful. They sing of big bowls of steaming rice. They sing of a pipe of tobacco waiting for them upon their return. Yes, and sometimes they are so daring as to mention a piece of bacon coming along with the rice. A piece of bacon, which they can hardly afford to buy once a year. Yes, the Chinese boat people are very poor.

A BRAVE RIVER MAN

CHAPTER IX

A BRAVE RIVER MAN

I WILL tell you a story of a brave river man.
As I told you before, our place was next to
the gate which led down to the harbor, the mouth
of the River Han. The harbor was filled with
hundreds of junks. There were so many boats
that you could walk from one deck to another.
In the middle of the harbor was a passageway for

two single lines of boats, one moving up and one moving down stream. The River Han is very quiet and is yellow tinted. But in spring, when the snow melts on the high peaks of Tibet, where the river has its source, the water swells and becomes very dangerous, and on certain days all the ships move out, leaving the whole harbor empty. Then whirling waters shoot down into the open arm of the big river Yangtze Kiang. One day a terrible disaster happened. Here is what I heard about it:

Whenever spring sets in suddenly with a hot day the waters rush down from the mountains in a wall more than six feet high. Now the Chinese are prepared for this; all along the Han River there are little station houses with a signal system for reporting from one to another that the wave is coming and that the harbor has to be cleared. Spring is also the time when in this country a terrible sickness—cholera—year by year sweeps over the land. On a certain day the signalman, Wei, at the station Wu Tien, had watermelon for breakfast, and cholera struck him before noon. While he was stretched out on his bed the wave came thundering down and passed his station. It passed the next station before the man there could give the signal. The harbor was crowded with junks. It was late in the afternoon, when everybody was busy preparing supper. A beautiful smell of fish fried in tea oil was hovering about the masts. Then a wave more than eight feet high broke into the harbor. It was like a hungry wolf breaking into a sheep herd, with white foaming teeth. The outcry of thousands mingled with thundering waters and breaking ship boards and masts. Fire ran out over the planks, climbed the masts, and ate the old sails and dry ropes.

In a moment the whole port was a mass of flames. On the bank, opposite the gate, was a factory for pressing wood oil out of the green fruits

77

of the wood-oil tree. Right in front of the factory was a pier, and tied to the pier was a foreign steel ship waiting for cargo.

The air was filled with dark clouds and burning sparks. The wind was blowing toward the factory and the ship. Sparks began to fall down on the roofs of the building where people were busy extinguishing them with buckets of water. But soon the sparks grew to such an extent that here and there flames started up. Finally the men had to jump down and flee before they were caught. Now the big shed was all aflame. The roof broke down, and through the opening oil barrels and baskets came shooting up like rockets and exploded in the air. Fire fell from the sky, and the ground around the building, soaked with oil of many years, was aflame, too. Burning oil broke through the walls and came running down the banks and even out over the surface of the water. The foreign ship, dark and so far untouched by

In a moment the whole port was a mass of flames

the fire, stood out against the howling red background. Because the fire under her boilers was out the ship could not move and would soon be a prey to the flames also.

But then this happened:

From the cool waters of the Yangtze Kiang came sputtering a small rusty launch, her funnel red-hot, feeling her way through burning ships which floated down the river like torches. Nearer and nearer the launch came to the ship's hulk. The sailors on board the foreign ship ran to and fro, the captain held his megaphone to his mouth and shouted down something to the little launch. After that a rope flew through the air, which the owner of the launch fastened to his ship. Then he turned toward the opening of the River Yangtze Kiang. At first nothing moved. But after some further agitation on board the foreign ship one heard the noise of a swaying rudder. Then suddenly the big hulk shook, the little launch screamed and slowly pulled her big sister toward safety.

Night came. The last débris was swept away by fire or water, and the whole harbor was dark. Only the glowing ruins of the factory on the other side whispered the tale of gruesome happenings.

But in our street the people had a wonderful story to tell of the poor owner of the little rusty launch who had risked his life and his ship to save a big foreign ship. He received a reward of such magnificence that he became the president of the Chinese merchant fleet, which has beautiful steamboats between Shanghai and Hankow, the pride of all Chinese merchants along the river.

CHEATERS CHEATED

CHAPTER X

CHEATERS CHEATED

THE Chinese are great talkers. News of all kinds travels fast in China, faster than by letter or telegram in other countries. For it goes from mouth to mouth on the crowded streets, and from the streets spreads through the gates along the roads on which an unending line of travelers and carriers moves toward other cities. Here the

87

news is shouted from one traveler to another and is in the next city before the first hearer has stopped for a rest along the road.

I liked to read the tidings on the faces passing our desk.

One day faces were grave, for restless soldiers had been seen later than usual in a garrison near the town. One day everyone smiled, for a cheater had been cheated.

And this is how it came about:

Mr. Feng, the owner of a silver shop in the street around the corner, was out for the day.

His two assistants, left alone in the shop, decided to be very clever and to make a good profit on that day, so that when their master came back he would be pleased and raise their salaries.

But quite a time passed and no customer came in sight. Yes, there were people calling, but they were only beggars. Dirty and clad in rags they stood in the doorway and stretched out their bowls with thin bony arms. And you know you have to give the beggar a small coin. Everybody has to give because beggars are persistent and will stay in front of the building, perhaps calling up more and more members of their guild until no respectable customer will enter the shop.

And sometimes, if the shop owner is so stingy that even this will not induce him to give to the beggars, some sick and dying member of the beggar guild will drag himself right in front of the building and die there. Then the shop owner has to buy a coffin for the body—a coffin—about the most expensive thing in China, for wood is scarce. Moreover, if the beggar is from another town the stingy one may be obliged to send the body home to the beggar's native village, thus incurring great expense.

For every Chinaman wants to be buried in the place he came from. Rich merchants who transact their business in a province other than the one in which they were born keep their coffins ready during their lifetime, so that in case of death they may be transported home and so rest in peace.

Well, Mr. Feng's assistants used some rough words on the beggars, but they gave them coins from the bowl containing small cash which is kept on the counter of every Chinese shop for the special purpose of speeding the departure of beggars.

But look, was not somebody entering the shop? Both assistants waited upon him, and they were slightly disappointed when they heard his tale.

The customer said his name was Wang; that he had been supervising a cargo of bean oil to be shipped up the river; that the boat had left and that he was waiting for his remittance from his firm up the river. He said he needed cash right away and, pulling a ring from his finger, asked the assistants to exchange it for cash. The two looked at the ring and found that it was good gold. Just as they were about to take the ring to the back room to weigh it and to fix the price another man came in.

Mr. Wang's face became quite bright when he saw this man.

"There you are at last, and I hope you have brought the remittance."

"Yes," the other said, "I have it, and a letter, too, and I am sorry that I am late. But last night when we stayed in Wu Tien the gates were closed an hour early, since it was feared that the bands of the White Wolf were out for some mischief. So we had to stay in that town all night. But there is your silver and the letter."

Mr. Wang took both and turning toward the two assistants said:

"I am indeed relieved that I need not sell that ring. Here is a lump of silver, please exchange it for cash. And, by the way, do me a favor and read that letter to me, as I cannot read."

The two assistants took the letter and read that the remittance of twelve ounces of fine silver was herewith sent to him and that he was expected to return immediately to his home town in order to supervise the unloading of the various loads of bean oil arriving in the meantime.

Mr. Wang thanked them and asked them for the cash. The two assistants went to the office in back of the store and put the silver on the scales. When the hand came to a standstill it showed a weight of fourteen ounces.

"Do you see it?" said the one. "It is fourteen ounces. Two ounces more than announced in the letter."

"Here is our chance," said the other, "it's a profit of two ounces of fine silver if we only pay him cash for the twelve ounces, as stated in the letter."

The two assistants took the letter

"He does not know any better," agreed the first one. "We read to him that the lump was twelve ounces, and if we just go in and tell him that the weight is in accordance with the letter he certainly will not want to see the scales."

No sooner said than done. And when they informed Mr. Wang that the weight was correct he thanked them for their trouble, took the cash, and departed with his friend.

Life seemed rosy to the two assistants. They rubbed their hands and speculated as to what Mr. Feng, the owner, would say when he came back and found them to be so clever. . . .

In the midst of their rejoicing a neighbor came rushing into the shop. He was very much excited and burst forth:

"What did the two men want who were here a minute ago? Did you have business with them? I hope not! Don't you know that one of them is the swindler, Tee, who cheated Lo, the bean-oil dealer, last year?"

A shadow fell over the faces of the two assistants, but they recovered from their surprise and said:

"We have nothing to fear. He cashed some silver, and the weight was all right."

"Weight is not everything," said the neighbor.

"You had better see whether the silver is good."

The hearts of the two assistants sank, for in their eagerness to make an extra profit neither had thought of cutting the lump of silver open to find out whether it was good, as is customary with silver buyers when an unknown man comes to them.

With trembling hands they took the lump out of the safe, reached for the scissors with which to cut silver, and cut the lump in two.

"What a shame!" they exclaimed.

There it was, ordinary pewter in a shell of good silver. Tears ran down their cheeks, ruin lay before them, but perhaps it was not yet too late. They asked the neighbor to take care of the shop and rushed out to find the swindler.

After much searching they picked up his trail and presently found him happily seated in a restaurant, eating stewed shark fins. With him was his friend.

The two assistants rushed at him, grabbed him by the coat and shouted:

"Swindler! Swindler! Give us back our cash and take your silver, which is no good."

But the guilty one remained quite calm. The proprietor of the restaurant came from behind the counter and asked what was causing the disturbance.

The two assistants were quite ready with their explanations.

"He cashed this silver in our shop, and when he had gone we found that only the outside of the lump was silver and that the greater part was pewter."

With these words they put the two pieces on the table.

Mr. Wang looked at the pieces and said:

"Well, if it is my silver I am certainly sorry to see that it is bad. I did not know that. But," he continued, "how many ounces were in that silver? I am willing to pay you back the money. How much did my silver weigh?"

"Twelve ounces," they said, "at the rate of three dollars an ounce."

Mr. Wang took the two pieces and, addressing the owner of the restaurant, said:

"Please, Mr. Dao, bring your silver scales and let's see whether this weighs twelve ounces."

The proprietor produced the scales, put them on the table, and placed the silver on them.

All eyes were fixed on the indicator. It came to a standstill—to a firm stop—on the mark of fourteen ounces.

The five faces around the table showed very different expressions. The two swindlers were undisturbed, even smiling; the two assistants had ashen faces; and the proprietor holding the scales sent a questioning look around.

"There, there," said Mr. Wang. "Fourteen ounces. Thus it cannot be my silver. For you

99

weighed my silver and said it was twelve ounces only, and cash for twelve ounces only I received."

Then, turning to Mr. Dao, Mr. Wang continued:

"What do you think of this? These two boys are trying to make me believe I sold them some bad silver."

But by this time the two assistants had snatched the two pieces of metal on the table and hastily withdrawn. For Mr. Dao was a strong man, eating shark fins all the time, and he looked as if he were just seeking an opportunity to exercise his fists. They went back to their shop and there fearfully awaited the return of their master.

This tale was long alive in our street, and honest people told it often as proof that dishonesty can only be beaten by honesty.

I AM LOST AND FOUND AGAIN

CHAPTER XI

I AM LOST AND FOUND AGAIN

IN THE excitement of observing the life around me and listening to the stories told at our table, I had forgotten all about myself. Good gracious, how different I looked! In fact, there was not much to be seen of me. All rubbed off. Just perhaps half of me left.

Where was the golden dragon that once shone on my back? Nothing left. Where was the golden name on my chest? All gone. But I had one satisfaction: what was gone was decorating paper with beautiful characters, carrying messages in all four directions.

To the north, where the cold wind blows, where endless caravans of camels tread through the sand of the Gobi Desert. Where for hundreds of years the capital had stood, its famous gates reaching up into the clouds. Where along the border there runs a wall bigger than a house and so wide that two carriages can travel side by side and still make room for a third one. Where in winter the rivers are dead and cannot say a single word because they have turned into ice—ice, which I have never seen. Then people walk on the river—not only walk, but run. Faster than a deer they go, because they put an iron blade under one foot, while around the other they wrap a rag to push them along. They call it skating.

In that capital in the north there once reigned an old empress, who killed sons and nephews so that she might remain on the throne; who drowned her son's most beloved wife in a well so that a crown prince might not be born. And when the foreigners came to punish her, because foreigners were being attacked and killed, she fled from the capital in a washerwoman's clothes. Outside the gates a sedan chair containing her imperial gowns waited for her. She sent out word to all the towns and villages that she, the mother of the country, was coming to visit them. And the people believed her, repaired the roads, and prepared festivals in her honor. Meanwhile the capital was conquered by the foreigners, and old people hanged themselves because the mother of the country had fled. . . .

Messages set down by my letter writer went to the south—the south of China, where palm trees grow; where the West River forms the big delta near the town of Canton, and where up to this day pirates attack the boats on the delta and then disappear in one of the refuges offered by the thousand arms of the river. To the south, where lies Hongkong, the pearl of the southern coast, conquered and held to this day by foreign people, who come from a small island in the west, called England. Do you know why this place was conquered by the English? I will tell you.

Seventy-five years ago the English had a big company in Canton, the southern capital, where they transacted all sorts of business. All other ports of China were closed to the foreigners. Every year the manager of the company had to go to the Viceroy of Canton to pay him a visit. And the manager had to begin his conversation with the words:

"My humble country offers her greetings."

In that year there was a manager who said: "It

is not a humble country. It is a wonderful country, and I shall not say, 'My humble country.'"

And he did not say it. He just said: "My country." Whereupon the Viceroy stamped his feet, and there was war. And the English won. . . .

Messages went to the east, perhaps as far as Japan. It is the country where the sun rises, therefore we call it Ja-pan. "Ja" means sun and "pan" means origin.

The Japanese are very clever, but they borrowed our characters for their writing. They took our art and developed it into something very new but the soul of it is Chinese.

Messages flew through the west. The west, where the sun goes down. To Tibet, the country with the highest mountains in the world. Its people have to come down every year to our capital to pay a tribute. But they do not allow any foreigners to come into their country.

In all these places of the earth you will now

find a speck of myself. Cannot I be happy that I carry messages into all these countries? Why should I cry that there is little left of my body, when my soul travels through wide spaces? And you know, a paper with writing on it is never thrown away in our country. A written slip with paper is something holy. When a little piece is found in the street the person who sees it picks it up and takes it to an altar, where it is burned and its ashes sent to heaven.

Just now, just at the moment when I boasted about my importance as a messenger, I was doing the finest thing in the world. I was expressing wishes for happy days. Mr. Wu, my master, sat all day long writing the character *"Fu"* on square pieces of red paper. One after another he finished them, and they were sold as soon as they were dry. For the New Year was approaching, and at the New Year everybody buys these posters to paste on the house doors. The word *"Fu"* means everything that is lucky, and you know New Year's is the day when we wish each other good fortune. But we do more than extend wishes. All the men in town are busy squaring their dealings with other men, and everyone pays his debts. When a business man opens his books on the first day of the new year the pages are blank, and there is no figure put down to indi- cate that he owes anything.

Thus our business was going well. One day it was so good that Mr. Wu called a passing fisher- man and asked him to show us the contents of his bucket. The fisherman stopped and said:

"It's a carp, Mr. Wu, and a very good one. I do not think that you will buy it."

Mr. Wu was a little hurt and replied:

"Can't you see that I am writing the word *'Fu'*? When writing such a beautiful character one has to have the best food, otherwise the char- acter loses its dignity. Show me the fish." And he bought the fish, although it cost him a lot of money. But his pride was hurt, and he wanted to show the fisherman that he was a man of position. Well, the carp was hung up in the shade of our roof, and everybody passing by admired it.

But around noontime it was hot, and Mr. Wu leaned back in his chair and took a little nap. At that moment a cat came strolling around the corner. Of course she, too, admired the carp. She became, in fact, very much interested in it. She crouched down, and the black in her eyes grew very small while she looked up at the fish. Then she licked her chops and crouched down more and more. Finally, what do you thing that cat did? She jumped on Mr. Wu's lap, and from there still higher up and began to claw the fish with both paws. Mr. Wu woke up with a start. When he saw what the cat was doing he screamed and jumped out of his chair. Up went the table and down went everything on it. The red papers,

Up went the table and down went everything on it

taken by the wind, sailed merrily through the air. The cup with the brushes landed in the middle of the street, and so did the tray on which I rested. When this came down on the pavement I got a terrific bump which landed me between two granite stones that form the pavement of Chinese streets. There I rested. Very soon feet began to walk over the hole in which I lay, and apparently I was lost. Night came. The street was very quiet. A few people carrying paper lanterns in their hands hurried home; and then all was still.

Dawn came and the new life of the street began. I heard the monotonous song, "Ho-he-ho-he-ho-he," of the water carriers, but I could not see anything. After a while a pair of small feet stopped near by; a little hand came down and a little finger began to poke in my resting place. Soon I felt myself being lifted, and then I found myself in the hands of a little boy, who looked at me triumphantly and carried me away.

AT THE TEA MERCHANT'S

CHAPTER XII

AT THE TEA MERCHANT'S

THE little boy was carrying me home. We went around the corner toward the river and soon entered a large house. The boy's father was a dealer in tea, and his home made me open wide my black eyes. It was right at the waterfront, and although it was late in the afternoon activities

117

were still going on. Ships were tied to the bank in front of the house, and coolies were unloading hundreds of square boxes, all pasted with colorful papers showing beautiful Chinese scenes.

The room behind the one opening onto the street was rather dark. In the middle was a round revolving table with little cups containing tea. About the table were standing foreigners who took a sip from one cup and then turned the table and took a sip from the next, and so on. Finally they marked the spot before a certain cup with a piece of chalk. Then they called for Mr. Lo, the boy's father, told him that they liked this tea and offered him a price.

One of the men was a Russian in a loose blouse. He looked at some boxes containing only tea dust, asked the price, and gave Mr. Lo a big order for tea dust. Can you imagine anyone buying tea dust? There was not a leaf in the boxes, just dust, black dust, with a smell of tea about it.

But I know what the Russians do with this dust. They buy enormous quantities of it and take it to a factory. There the tea dust is exposed to scalding steam. When it is all hot and mushy they pour it into iron forms and press it into bricks, which after they have dried are hard as a stone and very shiny. These bricks are sent to the north and to the west, and all the people of Tibet and Mongolia have the bricks in their houses and tents. Tea dust is just as essential to them as bread to Americans. The people chop the brick to pieces and boil it with lard and fat into a soup which is the national dish. After you have been out in the cold all day and have come back to a tent which has no stove there is nothing so good as a steaming bowl of tea soup.

In a Chinese house tea is always ready. It is served in little cups with the saucers on top of them. If you pay a formal visit you do not touch the tea until you want to show the host that it is time for you to go. Then you take a sip—if possible, with much noise, to show the host that you are enjoying it. We do not put cream or sugar in our tea: it is just some hot water on top of a few fragrant leaves. And it is drunk winter and summer. The Chinese never take cold drinks. If a Chinaman wants to offer beer and wine to a foreigner he offers them warm. The Chinese wine called *"Sam Tchu"* and made from rice is offered in tiny little China cups and almost steaming hot.

Behind the business quarters of Mr. Lo's house we passed through a corridor which had beautifully carved window frames on the right. Instead of glass panes, the openings were covered with paper, which is very practical. First of all, the thin white papers give smooth light without a glare. Then, when it is very hot and you want some more air, you just break the paper and in comes the fresh air. When you have had enough air, a new sheet of paper is placed over the opening.

The wall on the left side of the corridor was

closed except for a round opening, an opening as round as the full moon. The Chinese call it the "moon view." Through this opening one could see the garden between the business quarters and those of the family. What a beautiful view! The garden was laid out so that it presented its finest aspect through the opening. There was a little group of rocks in the middle, and flowers and little trees growing in china pots. A little pool with fresh water reflected mirrorlike a bit of the sky, and goldfish swam about in it. Shining pebbles covered the ground of the pool and were laid around the stems of the trees and plants.

A cage with a Chinese nightingale hung on one of the wooden pillars. Toward sunset the boy's father takes the cage and goes to a green spot near the city hall. Here he meets other lovers of birds, all carrying their pets in cages with them. They put the birds on the grass and enjoy an hour's rest, their hearts filled with happiness at seeing their pets nibbling at the grass sprouts and sending evening songs toward the golden sky.

At the end of the corridor we came to the family quarters. The meal was all ready and the table

The "moon view"

set. There were many children, and the mother was the best in town. She walked slowly with a stiff step, because her feet were crippled from binding. In former years the Chinese used to bind their daughters' feet to keep them small.

My boy loved his mother, as his heart and the education of centuries prompted him to do. There is no law in China greater than that which bids us honor our fathers and mothers. No one can go to heaven unless his children pray for his soul and put up an altar in the house for their dead. The altar must be kept well supplied with dishes of food, incense sticks, and a bronze bowl containing imitation money which is burned from time to time.

Do you know what Meng, from Ningpo, did for his mother? It is an old story. I will tell you.

MENG FROM NINGPO

CHAPTER XIII

MENG FROM NINGPO

MENG'S father had died, and he was providing for his mother. But the strip of land he had inherited became sterile, and hunger faced them both. Meng decided to go to a northern district, where the crops were manifold during the year. But his mother could not walk. He had no money to rent a cart, but go he must, if he wanted to keep his mother alive. So he took his old mother on his back and walked out of his native district, begging for their meals. He walked hundreds of miles with his old mother on his back and then at last they arrived at the valley of many crops. The people there were happy, and friendly with the newcomers. And when they heard how Meng had carried his mother on his back for hundreds of miles they gave him a little hut and seed to plant in a strip of land. But when the first green sprouts appeared the mother fell sick, and she felt her end coming. As you know, a Chinese always wants to die on the ground where he was born. But, alas! her native land was far away.

The son saw his mother's suffering. He stood at the door and saw the green rice in all its promising beauty. A light wind gently ruffled the green patch, and the little stems bowed and whispered a tale of coming days when they would stand high and yellow in the warm sun, their feet

He walked hundreds of miles with his old mother on his back

in nourishing water, and their heads bowed under the burden of ripe grain.

The son heard it all, and he saw himself starting out in the morning and coming home at night with bundles of brown stalks filling his pots with golden rice, enough to keep them both happy and content and enough to put back in the clean soil for another crop. But when he turned into the hut he saw his mother's eyes burning with longing to see that native village for the last time, before they closed forever. Then Meng did not hesitate another moment.

133

Gently he took the old woman on his back, grasped a stick and the begging bowl, and started out. He walked back all the hundreds of miles, begging, and tending his mother until at last they arrived at their bare old home. But to his mother it was like the gate to heaven. She sank down on the old bedstead and, glancing around, died with a happy smile on her old lips.

The son buried her in the place where she and he had been born, and, although his life was full of hunger and deprivation, Meng never left the spot where the little hill covered his mother's remains.

I AM DISCOVERED

CHAPTER XIV

I AM DISCOVERED

BUT now we must come back to this new home of mine. The meal was served. Everybody from the shop and the house was called, and soon the whole family, as well as the assistants in business, were gathered around the big round table. In the middle of the table stood several bowls with salted beans, cooked cabbage, and pork cut in small slices. In China nothing is cut at the table, and there is no knife to be seen.

When everybody was seated a coolie went around and served big bowls of steaming white rice. The men took up the bowls with their left hands, using the chopsticks in the right to shovel the rice into their hungry mouths. From time to time the chopsticks reached over the table and picked up with great skill a single salted bean, a leaf of cabbage, or a piece of pork. The pork they dipped into a sauce which one found in a bowl also in the middle of the table.

When my little boy, whose name was Liang, started to eat, his mother saw that he was trying to eat the rice without lifting the bowl. Instead he held his left fist clutched tightly around me. She asked him to open his hand and very reluctantly he did so. There I was, right in the light of the big kerosene lamp which hung over the table. Twenty astonished eyes were fixed on me, and ten mouths stood still, then began to move and open, and soon to laugh and to chatter. There was no end of astonishment and excitement about the stick of ink in the little boy's hand.

The chief accountant, an old man with several hairs on each side of his upper lip and enormous glasses on his nose, held by two silk cords fastened behind his ears, made quite a speech and prophesied that it was a good sign that the boy had picked me up and treasured me that way: he certainly would become a very learned man.

139

Liang's father was so pleased with this outlook that he told the boy he would take him to the spring procession the next morning.

"And may I take my stick of ink with me?" asked Liang.

"You certainly may," said the father, "and I am going to give you a pewter box to keep it in so that there will be no prints in your hand such as there are now."

THE SPRING FESTIVAL

CHAPTER XV

THE SPRING FESTIVAL

THIS was a long night for Liang. He had never seen a spring procession. When the sun rose at last he dressed hastily. It was already warm, so his whole garment consisted of a pair of trousers cut out back and front and a little jacket. His head was shaved except for four or five tufts of hair, which were twisted into little pigtails fastened with colored wool.

After breakfast Liang's father took him to his office and presented him with the pewter box, which had a picture of two cranes on the lid. I was put into this box, but Liang kept opening it every minute, taking me out and holding me in his hand, so that I could easily see what was going on around me.

We were in the midst of the crowd that pressed toward the East Gate. Here we waited, and soon music came nearer and nearer.

There was the band: flutes and clarinets and gongs which were beaten frantically. Behind the band marched the magistrate. He wore dark blue gowns of silk, and on the front and back of his jacket were squares embroidered in many colors showing a peacock. That meant that he was of the third degree. On his cap was a clear blue glass knob. He smiled and bowed, and his escort walked behind him in a very formal way. All the men of the escort wore badges on their chests and backs. One had a pheasant design, another a duck, and yet another a wild goose, showing that they were all of lesser degree than the magistrate. The knobs on their caps were of white crystal, of dark blue glass or of cloudy crystal.

Behind the escort pressed the crowd. The whole procession was swallowed by the dark mouth of the East Gate. We followed too, and when we reached the open we saw the magistrate kneeling toward the sun, surrounded by men carrying an image of a cow painted in gaudy yellow colors, which means that the crops will be plentiful. There was also an image of the local god with bare feet and bare head, symbolizing dry weather, which the people wished to have for the coming weeks.

When the magistrate had finished his kotow there was more frantic music, and the procession started to move back to the gate. To kotow means to touch your head to the ground, and it is the sign of highest respect. Some beggars in the street do it constantly, and to arouse the pity of passers-by they knock their heads with such force that their foreheads are all swollen and one terrible wound.

AT HOME WITH LIANG

CHAPTER XVI

AT HOME WITH LIANG

WE FOLLOWED the procession until we
came back to the house on the river bank.
When we arrived there I felt very happy in the
midst of the family. Soon the new surroundings
were to me a matter of course.

Liang cherished me and took me wherever he

went. Mostly without my case, as his little belt was not big enough to hold it.

Chinese children have very few toys. Although Liang's father was considered to be a rich man, the boy's toys consisted only of a simple wooden sword which the head coolie had fashioned for him one day, and a pig made of earthenware with a slot on his back for coins. There were always a few coins in the pig, and to Liang it was not only a savings bank but a musical instrument as well. He shook the pig when he danced with the other children in a quiet street around the corner where no traffic disturbed their play.

There were quite a number of children of the same age who used to meet in this street, and what excitement two old metal marbles could create for them.

The men selling candies always went through this street and made the little mouths water.

There were beautiful things in his basket, such as candied coconut, ginger and sugared bits of melon cut up into squares. The little earthen pig which we usually had with us would be shaken like a thunderstorm until a coin slipped out and went into the belt of the sweetmeat dealer.

But what are candies compared with pickles?

Do you hear the rattle around the corner? It is the pickle hawker.

Oh, look at the wonderful things all dripping with vinegar!

There are unripe mangoes, sliced cucumbers, and carambolas.

"Where is the pig? Hawker, you wait! I'll fetch the money."

And the hawker waits. The small voice is commanding. It has been trained from the beginning to imitate that of the grown-ups, be it in a polite way—asking one's neighbor very formally: "Did you eat your rice, Mr. Wang?"

which means, "How do you do, Mr. Wang"; or
be it in a harsh, commanding way, just as Father

talks when the coolies make too much noise in
the warehouse.

Yes, the hawker waits, and the pig is emptied
after a good deal of shaking. And soon the
pickles bought have disappeared, and only a little
taste of vinegar on one's fingers reminds one of a

minute of heaven on earth. Well, there are many visitors in Father's house, and if they do not see the pig standing on the corner table it is put right under their noses, and it squeaks, "I am hungry."

Do you know the Ping Pom man, the man who sells white and red glass ping poms? He often passes the house, and sometimes Father gives us ten cash to buy a ping pom, which, alas! does not last very long. Ping poms consist of small glass tubes which widen at one end like a trumpet. But the end is not open. A thin film of glass covers it. You put the other end in your mouth and blow gently. Gently, gently! I said. That's it! And then a sound like ping-pom, ping-pom, comes from the vibrating membrane covering the wider end of the little instrument. But if you blow hard— kling-ling it goes, and it is broken. Ping poms are a source of immense delight to the children, just because they break whenever you think, "Now it sounds good."

There is always something new in the street, which makes the children happy.

See the old man stopping in front of the warehouse. Slowly he settles down. A wooden tablet with a white lacquered surface is placed on his knees. A box is opened. Out of it he takes a piece of ink which he begins to rub with water on a tray. Adults and children gather. Now he has rubbed enough ink to start, but where is his brush? What is he doing without a brush? There, he dips a finger into the ink and begins. In a few seconds he has drawn with his finger the picture of a crane. The beak and the eye of the bird are being done with his pointed finger nails.

Aiii!—how we marvel at the skill of the man drawing without a brush. But the artist does not rest long. A rag blots out the drawing, and out of his black finger runs the picture of a beautiful phœnix with a long, waving tail. And now coins begin to fall into the lap of the artist, who be-

The beak and eye of the bird are being done with his pointed finger nails

comes quite excited, blots out the old drawing, and starts again. In a moment's time he has finished the picture of a lotus flower.

"*Hao, hao,*" murmurs the crowd. And that is just like hand clapping in western countries.

We follow the old man for a long time, and if it were not time for dinner we should never, never come home again.

A LONG JOURNEY

CHAPTER XVII

A LONG JOURNEY

ONE day I noticed a lot of excitement in the house. Liang's father was going up the river to visit his brother, who was the owner of many tea plantations in the neighborhood of the town of Changsha.

Liang was to accompany his father, and I was going too! I was tucked securely away in the pewter case.

At night we left the house. Our luggage was all stowed away in baskets. We took mattresses with us and a pot of hot tea, for a drink has to be handy during the warm night. Many friends were assembled on the pier where our steamer was moored, and when we stepped on the gangway thousands of crackers were blown off, gongs were beaten with force, and all the evil spirits that had gathered to make our journey unhappy were driven away by the infernal noise. Slowly our steamer turned into the darkness of the big river.

We stayed up for a while, and when we had passed our town and come to the villages where the boatmen live we beheld a wonderful sight. It was the night of the Spirit's Festival. Down the river came little boats, bearing lanterns, which were floated by the people living on the river banks to lighten the darkness of the waters and as a sacrifice to those whose deaths have been occa-

sioned by water. The little lights came and went;
they passed our steamer and floated quietly down
the river. Some of them began to dance on little
waves caused by our boat. And some of them who
came so near to us that we saw the little flickering
candle in the lanterns, were suddenly swallowed
by the bigger wave from the bow of our ship.

Soon it was dark again, and a sailor hung over-
board throwing the line into the black gurgling
water, pulling it up and reading the depth of the
water in a monotonous singing way: "Threeee
threee quart'r." I heard it all night and thought
of the danger of sand banks and whirling waters.

Nobody, apparently, slept on this ship. Only
Liang lay down on his mattress, holding me in
his hand. But when he fell asleep his little hand
opened a bit, and I could see the life around me
going on merrily through the night. Most of the
men sat down to gamble. Some drank tea, and
some had wine with them. They played one very

noisy game in which two people shouted at each other like madmen. It was all about guessing the number of fingers stretched out by both at the same time. The two players sit confronting each other. Their right hands are closed to a fist and held in front of their faces. Down go the fists— once, twice—and at the third time each of the two players stretches out a number of fingers and both shout at the top of their voices the number of fingers stretched out. The one who guesses right wins, but the rewarding drink goes to the loser. Yet after playing this for hours the one who has lost most of the time and had to take many drinks is the real loser. For the strong rice wine overpowers him and makes him lie down with his face all purple, grunting like a sick man.

In the morning we reached the town of Changsha, our destination. Thousands were waiting on the bank of the river for the arrival of our boat. There stood the hordes of coolies with their poles, all shouting loud and offering their services. Hotel clerks frantically waved long white paper sheets with the names and addresses of their hotels. Sellers of sweetmeats, pickles, small breads, and steaming white rice sat in rows, all busy with fans to chase the hungry flies away. Beyond these were the ricksha coolies, energetically turning the pillows so that the expected passengers might have cool seats.

The police were engaged in keeping the crowd back with long bamboo sticks which descended on heads and shoulders without mercy. But when our gangway was down the police were powerless. The army of the coolies swept through them with yells and waving poles, and jumped and climbed on the deck of our boat, seizing whatever luggage they could get hold of to secure a first meal for the day. Never have I seen such struggling and heard such shouting.

Liang's father knew all about this beforehand.

He had gathered our luggage and the mattresses and sat on top of them like a general defending a fortress. Again and again the coolies tried to pull the mattresses away from him and to force him to accept their services. But Father was always successful in keeping the things together; even the teapot on his lap was safe, although empty.

After a while a young man in a long light blue gown appeared before us and presented his red visiting card and a letter saying that he was an assistant of Mr. Fo, father's brother, and had come to take care of us. Father came down from his fortress, since the polite assistant had brought with him some house coolies, who now took our bundles. Soon we all marched over the gangway and up the steps of the bank.

We took several rickshas, and off we went. We went through the whole town, bumping along over the rough granite pavement of the streets and practically always in cooling shade. This town is much hotter than our home town, and the owners of the houses lay bamboo sticks from one roof to another across the street, and on top of them matting or blue cotton cloth to keep the rays of the sun out of the streets.

On our way through the town we passed one street where are made all the embroideries for which this place is famous. They are done in one color only, namely gray on white silk. But the gray runs through all shades. The subjects are mostly birds and flowers. The work is done by men, and I could see them sitting in the open shops, their yellow faces bent over the wooden frames which keep the pieces of silk stretched even. They had no patterns to look at, but created the beautiful designs out of their heads, just as their fathers and forefathers had done for centuries.

We left the town through the North Gate and soon came to a small river, or rather creek. There we climbed out of the rickshas and went on board a junk. The old raggedy sail was hoisted, and we began to move quietly down the river toward the lake, whose blinking surface could be detected through the willow trees in front of us. After half an hour's delightful sailing we came to the lake. We sailed along the eastern bank, and there for the first time I saw live cranes. There were thousands of them, standing on one leg in the shallow water. Their heads were black, and around their eyes were brilliant red rings—as red as the lacquered tray on which I began my life. Their feathers were of a delicate gray. They were not at all disturbed by our coming, just took a look and went on with fishing and cleaning their feathers.

But then we rounded a corner and sailed right into the midst of a swarm of wild swans, who rose, beating the waters and honking, and filling the blue sky with great white wings. Little white feathers came down, like the snow of which the

On the lake

wild men from the north used to speak when they came to Mr. Wu's desk.

I was longing for the atmosphere of Mr. Kao Ko Kung's studio. Better still, I wished I were with an artist who painted birds. I would gladly have given my little black body to help him draw those beautiful forms.

We crossed the lake and entered another creek, which soon ended. There were stone steps and a high stone gate, and at the gate stood Mr. Fo to bid us welcome.

The houses—there were quite a number of them as well as warehouses and sheds—were surrounded by stone oaks, and behind them rose the hills where the tea grew. We saw the little dark green trees, round like melons and planted in long rows running over the hills.

Every one of the next days brought something new to see. We went through the long rows of tea trees where the workmen picked the young leaves. We went through the wide yards where the green leaves are first exposed to the air for two or three hours. And then we went through the shed where the leaves, after having been dried in the sun, are spread on iron pans over open fires. The men keep the pans moving constantly for about five minutes for every filling. After that the roasted leaves go to big tables, where they are rolled by hand till all the juice is pressed out and they become little twisted rolls such as you have seen in the tea box.

After that they go back to the sun and back to the table till they are all well dried and well curled and ready to be packed into the lead-lined chests with the gay colored pictures outside, such as I had seen being carried into our father's house on the river.

We stayed for several days, and I was admired by everybody. Never have I forgotten the astonished face of the old grandmother when she saw me in Liang's hand. "What will the world come to," she said, "when such little children already carry ink with them? They will all be writers and learned men, and there will be nobody to go out and pick tea."

The earthen pig had gone with us and was duly admired and its belly filled with many pieces of cash. The pickle hawker will have to come twice a day for a while before that pig's stomach will be emptied.

Mostly I loved the nights in the country. The moon stood high over the silver lake. The crickets sang all night, and from the cool water came the murmurs of the birds.

Summer was here. Glaring hot summer in China. Not a stir of wind. The faces yellow-pale and the bodies perspiring. The mosquitoes hung in clouds over the villages and hummed their bloodthirsty song all night. The sleepers put bare mattresses out in the open, and their hands moved their fans incessantly during the night, even while they slept.

We went home the way we came. Soon we were all reunited again. And soon the pig's stomach was empty.

THE NEW YEAR

CHAPTER XVIII

THE NEW YEAR

WHEN the summer was over the boy's mother let his hair grow, and by the following New Year he wore the same headdress as the grown-ups. The little pigtails in the back were gone. His head was shaven in front, and the hair in the back grew longer and longer and was twisted into a queue which began to hang down over Liang's collar. Where it ended a beautiful black silk cord was twisted into it and hung down his back, ending in two black tassels.

New Year was approaching, and I saw the square red papers pasted on the front doors of the houses with the character *"Fu"* written on them. The boy's father was busy closing his accounts, and in the kitchen preparations were being made for a big meal for the many people of the house.

When the day came the boy's father took his son with him to visit his friends. Liang was dressed the same way as his father, in long dark blue gowns and a silk jacket with wide sleeves. He did his best to imitate his father's poise, walking stiffly and bowing to the neighbors. On his little nose he even wore a pair of big spectacles. The pig was in one hand, and I lay in the pewter box, which was stuck into the silk scarf around the boy's waist.

Coolies went with us and carried presents, such as silk and tea in small boxes.

No need to shake the pig to-day. Candies and pickles were offered in every house. Moreover, coins were freely dropped into the slot in the pig's back, until on the way home it became quite a burden.

At night the street was full of noise, and millions of crackers burst loose.

Liang stayed up half the night, although all day he had been trudging along by his father's side in his fine toggery to pay the New Year calls. *"Kung Hsi Fa Tsai,"* he had said at least a hundred times, bowing and scraping and shaking his chubby little fingers in exact imitation of his father.

SCHOOL DAYS

CHAPTER XIX

SCHOOL DAYS

THE following spring the father gave a big dinner to his relatives and friends. It marked the day when Liang got his "school name." You see, Liang was his "milk name"; now he got the name of Tsang, the Faithful One. Under this name he now became known to his teacher and to his friends in school, but his mother still called him Liang.

Very soon we saw the teacher for the first time.

The schoolroom was only a few blocks from the house and was kept by several well-to-do families, who paid the teacher's wages. When the school day came I was put into the pewter box and together with the necessary paper and a brush we made our way to the schoolhouse.

There were about twenty boys in the room. They had finished reciting and were all busy writing. They wrote on white tissue paper which they had placed on top of a piece of cardboard. This cardboard had four black squares, in each of which was a white character. The boys were trying to follow the outlines of the character with their brushes, thus producing a black character on the tissue paper. This is the way a Chinese child learns to write: by tracing characters for years and years, until his hand does it mechanically.

Then they begin to read aloud, and all they read they have to learn by heart and say to the teacher with their backs turned toward him. Since everyone recites at the same time the school is about the noisiest place imaginable; you can easily find a school in any street.

The teacher was an old man, who wore, of course, big spectacles in tortoise-shell frames. He had a mole on the left side of the chin, out of which grew three hairs. They were long hairs which he stroked incessantly with a little comb. The Chinese has not much of a beard, and anyone who has hair growing on his face is very proud of it and cultivates and combs it carefully.

The Chinese school children have no Saturday or Sunday holidays. They do not know what a half day off is, and they study from daylight to dark. They have no different classes for geography, arithmetic, and the like. All they do is practise writing and reading. For years they do not know the meaning of what they read. The understanding comes much later. They copy and read old classic books. The first one is the "Three

Character Book" which begins with the sentence:

"Men at their birth are by nature good."

And here I want to tell you something more about the Chinese written language. The Chinese language has no alphabet. Each word is a character, which consists of from one to seventeen different strokes.

Writing was invented in China five thousand years ago, and in the beginning one wrote with a stylus upon small wooden tablets. Later on one began to use a wooden pencil which one dipped in black varnish. The writing was done on strips of silk. After that the brush was invented and one began to write on paper.

There are forty thousand known characters. It is said that the great Chinese philosopher Confucius knew them all. But a well-educated man usually knows only four thousand.

In the years when writing was first invented it

was used only in messages to the government, and the common people did not know much of it. One day, when a palace burned down, all these

messages were thrown out of the windows. When the people in the street saw the curious black markings they said:

"Look at all the tadpoles."

That is exactly what Chinese characters look

like, with their big heads and slender tails.

Every year new characters are invented, or rather composed, because new words turn up, mostly from foreign countries. A special committee is busy forming these new characters. For instance, when the first railroad came to China they had no name for it. So the committee sat down and composed a character for "railroad." They took the character representing "carriage" and put the character for "fire" in front of it and made known to the Chinese world that this was the name for the fire-spouting carriage which ran without a horse.

When the telephone came to the country and the first wires were put up between Shanghai and Wusung the committee got to work at once and found a character for this new thing. They took the character for "cord" and put the character for "lightning" in front of it, and there was the telephone.

a roof

a pig

Djia = the family, home

In fact, most of the characters are composed this way. Let's look at a few.

A roof with a pig and a man beneath it is the character for "family," for a man who has a house with a pig—that is, something to eat—can start to raise a family.

And see what they do with the character for "heart." If you look at it you will see that it is just a little picture of a heart. If you put the two characters meaning "heart" and "to speak" together you get a composite character which means "to rejoice." Isn't it wonderful? A heart that speaks is certainly rejoicing. But if you put a knife in front of the heart it means "grief." And if you write the two characters for "small heart" it means "attention"; you will find these two characters at railway crossings, I think that is an excellent way of expressing it, for in case of danger the heart contracts and calls attention to what is happening.

191

Of course, sometimes there come to China words which cannot be translated; for instance, a name. Let us take the name of your country, America: the most important sound to the Chinese, when they first heard it, was the second syllable, *"Mei."* This they kept, and added to it the character "Guo" which means land. Now America in China is "Mei-Guo." Of course, for a big country like America the Chinese would not take just any character denoting the sound *"Mei."* The first Americans appearing in China 'came on big ships, and the news that spread about the country where these ships came from told of wonderful things. So the committee searched the old classics for a character *"Mei"* with a meaning which should do justice to all the splendor. They found it—one that means handsome, beautiful, excellent, and fine at the same time. . . .

The school lasted till late in the afternoon, but how proud we were when we came home and showed our first written characters to the family and then to the men working in the house.

The head coolie, who could not read or write, looked at the writing with big eyes, shook his head as if he understood something of writing, and from that day on called Liang *"Tsang Hsien Sheng,"* which means Mr. Tsang.

Gone were the days of play, for life was serious now and filled with studies. And one day it became very serious.

193

RUMORS OF WAR

CHAPTER XX

RUMORS OF WAR

EVER growing rumors of restless soldiers were spread through the city. Boats from up the river failed to appear, and one night fires flared up on the other side of the river, and shots were heard.

Toward dawn there were knocks at the door. Mr. Lo opened it, and into his arms fell his friend from Wuchang, the big city across the river. He was altogether exhausted.

And he brought the news of the uprising of the garrison. They had burned the palace of the viceroy, who had fled to his houseboat and sailed down the river. Mr. Lo's friend brought the news of thousands of poor coolies mixing with the soldiers and breaking into the houses and robbing those of the rich. He himself had escaped through the back door and crossed the river, rowing himself.

Mr. Lo went back into the house and woke up the family and his business assistants. He sent them out and ordered his wife to pack up the bedding and enough food for several days. Two carts arrived at the door, and everybody placed his belongings on top of them. In one the mother took her place, with the youngest baby in her arms. In the second rode the other children and the women of the household.

When my boy was made ready for the flight he took his paper and his brush in one hand. He took me in the other and seated himself in the second cart. Then we started. The North Gate was wide open, and everybody seemed to be fleeing from the city. Behind us we saw the horizon glowing with the fires in the city of Wuchang. We heard the volleys of shots distinctly through the night, as we proceeded along the road taking us away from the uproar and toward the safe region in the north.

My little boy fell asleep, his fingers clasping me tight. But very soon the little hand lost its grip; it opened slowly, and out I fell.

I fell and landed in the middle of the road.

And very soon thousands of feet passed over me.

When dawn came it began to rain. The road turned into a swamp, and deeper and deeper I sank into the mud.

Squish—squash—squish—squash go the feet of the carriers of burden. And then came the big wheel.

THE END